SUNDAY EXPRESS & DAILY EXPRESS
CARTOONS

FORTY-EIGHTH SERIES

Pedigree
BOOKS

Published by Pedigree Books Limited
The Old Rectory Metford Lane, Exeter, Devon, EX2 4PS
Under Licence from Express Newspapers plc.
Printed in Italy. ©1994 Express Newspapers plc.

£3.99

GI 48

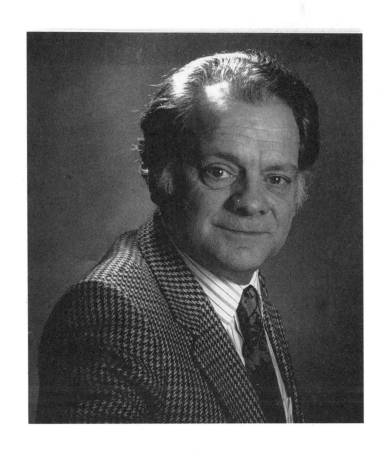

INTRODUCTION

by

DAVID

JASON

When mankind first learned to communicate the first joke was not far behind.

Laughter is one of the most precious gifts that the human race possesses. It takes us all, for a few fleeting moments, away from the pressure of everyday life; and those people who have the gift to make us laugh are very precious indeed.

Not many people can tell a story well and make us truly laugh, but I think Giles is one of our most gifted story-tellers, for what are cartoons if not funny stories told in a visual way, and in Giles' case by a brilliant teller?

Giles is as British as fish and chips and a pork banger, only funnier than both.
The day we have the standard Politically Correct E.U. Approved joke is the day the British will have no need of Giles.

Read on, take your time and enjoy yourself.

"They tell me they're still troubled with snow up North."

Daily Express, Feb. 11th, 1947

"Have you NO sense of duty - NO decent feelings ? Can't you manage just ONE extra for Easter?"

Sunday Express, Apr. 6th, 1947

"I wish someone'd hurry up and pinch this ——— bird if they're going to."

Daily Express, Dec. 9th, 1947

"You'll get more than you think you'll get if my wall isn't finished tonight."

Daily Express, Jan. 24th, 1952

"What makes me laugh is my wife spent the heat-wave at the sales fighting for a sun-suit."

Daily Express, Jul. 3rd, 1952

"Good idea asking your friend if we could help on his farm during the holidays, wasn't it ?"

"That would be from the bride and bridegroom you booked yesterday, Jack."

Daily Express, Feb. 2nd, 1965

"Oh dear, in his present militant mood Doctor isn't going to like that."

Sunday Express, Feb. 14th, 1965

"On the other hand there's nothing in the rules to say skis <u>can't</u> be worn."

Daily Express, Mar. 2nd, 1965

"Reminding me it was me who forgot that football started on the same day
as I booked our holiday don't help, either."

Sunday Express, Aug. 22nd, 1965

"Note from the office, Humphrey - the temporary man in your job is doing fine,
so you can take another week."

Sunday Express, Aug. 29th, 1965

"And now, if we have one virile, intelligent volunteer to turn the handle..."

(Headline: Schools urged to provide apples and machine to decore them)

Daily Express, Sep. 16th, 1965

"Hold your fire, men. Last minute reprieve from the Home Secretary on condition the prisoner doesn't clean his flick-knife on the school towel again."

Sunday Express, Mar. 6th, 1966

" 'Permitting a vehicle to be on the highway in an unroadworthy condition,' every one of them.
Best catch for a long time!"

Daily Express, Nov. 29th, 1966

"Grandma wasn't praying for World Peace - she was praying for her nap to come up in Wednesday's Derby."

Sunday Express, Jun. 4th, 1967

"Special treat for Father's Day - lunch with her mother."

Sunday Express, June 18th, 1967

" I'm not here to taste your grapes and toffee's just because you think they're trying to knock you off."

Sunday Express, Sep. 24th, 1967

"As a matter of fact that's <u>exactly</u> what I said in front of the children about their new Radio One."

Sunday Express, Oct. 1st, 1967

"He shouldn't be gone very long - he's got to be back to get his hamster's tea."

Daily Express, Oct. 31st, 1968

Daily Express, Jul. 23rd, 1968

How about one of those friendly cricket matches to create a better relationship between the Protest Marchers and the Police?

hi readers!

applause

normal service
will be
resumed as
soon as
possible

once again you will be glad to no that i am taking over
from mr giles who's busted his thum in an argument with
a rope on his boat. i don't think he's very happy about
this and wants to know why its always his thum that gets
busted and never any of his crews little thums. he says if
he busts it many more times he's going to learn to draw with
his feet and he don't like jokes about that probably being
a good idea anyway.

Some of his mates say he's ~~malingring~~ ~~the~~ ~~lucky~~
mlingring. on the tode in the hole all the time the newspaper
~~dispote~~ was on and he hasn't been back a couple of weeks
before he goes on the club. he says if they think you
can get a thum mended on the national health at the
london clink where he went they'll be ~~XXXXX~~ lucky.

yours truly,
giles junor

*
P.S.
the one marked with an arrow isn't me he's aunty vera's and
he aint very bright and ca'nt ~~rite~~ ~~write~~ rite in any case.

achtung line

hear me hear me.

When i asked mr giles if he wanted me to stand in for him and his busted thum again he said no ~~but~~ he didn't.

one thum g said evryone was fed up with his thum especially him, he had his stiches out today and he said O for each one and his more wiggly thanever and he says if i write another one of my letters it'll be me needing the stiches.

excuse me while i meditate on world affairs.

well thats enough of that. world affairs dont look very rosy wheather you're on you head or sitting ~~down~~ down. only one or (go to top of next col.)

(continued from down there)

two news items interest me. if i'd been the one to let the olympik torch go out like that fool did yesterday as soon as he'd landed in mixico i'd have sure got a thik ear from one thum g.

i see all the little doblin men are bopping one another as usual. mr g. likes doblin because it's where he first met irish coffee.

there's a story going about nurses going to get paper uniforms but mrg. says if he had his way he'd clap 'em all in irons. mrg. thinks all nurses are the enemy because they keep making him do evrything he dont want to do and they keep nicking his grapes and leaving him the stalks. (up you go)

(continued)

well i wont mention the tory confrance because one thum wo'nt let me get tied up in politics especially mr enok powell's.

well i must close now as i accidently changed mr g's antyseptic lotion for grandma's gin and i dont think its made him any appier. grandma's finished his antyseptic lotion and she dont look none the worse. she could do with a freshner in any case.

yours truly, giles junor.

P.S. butch our airdale was so pleased to see mr g. when he came home he jumped up to say allo, did hit mr g's thum. mr g said O again and so did butch.

P.S.

If anybody sees a silver-grey DB5 Aston Martin, registration number ELL 960C, please phone Scotland Yard as it belongs to 1 Thum G. and was nicked in Ipswich yesterday afternoon.—GILES JUNIOR.

this way up

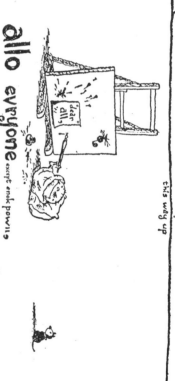

allo evryone except enok powlis

"well i hear i am still standing in and out for mr giles and his thum. his thums getting better and he's getting worse. he was ever so happy when he went to get his car and found it had been pinched." he went up in the air like a fig landing on a hot plate

evryone in sight was a potential car thief including aunty vera and the chief constable. one thum g. wanted to know why the police were hanging around on point duty instead of looking for his car. one newspaper reported that he was worried in case it had been stolen by little boys who could'nt drive fast cars ho ho ho theyll get hurt allright if one thum gets his other hand on em;

when a policeman found it in nottingham we had a roll call in the famly to see if any of us were in nottingham. grandma said it was/probably the policeman who found it that pinched to get back to nottingham and i said why did'nt they do a bank while they had it then i hid up.

i asked one thum if he would like me to report the tory confrence in gibralter or mr wilson and mr smith in blackpool and he said

well i must close now,
yours truly,
giles junor.

ps. one of my fans wrote to me and said 'dear illitrate pig, don't you know that the trobbles last sunday were in londonderry not doblin? i didn't say they were in doblin.
i said the little doblin men were having a bop up. doblin men can have a bop up in londondery can't they.
pps. one thum will be back next week if he don't blow up

"Grandma heard him say she was probably beating out *O Valiant Hearts* during the Crimean War."

Sunday Express, Nov. 10th, 1968

"That's enough confession for one day, O'Murphy - 123 addresses where you can get one after time less than a hundred yards from this very church."

Sunday Express, Oct. 19th, 1965

"You realise if you sign, daddy, it also means that you must not lay a finger on Timothy if he invades the pitch."

Sunday Express, Mar. 15th, 1970

Sunday Express, Aug. 9th, 1970

"A particle of clothing was taken from the Chancellor of the Exchequer today. Police are looking for a rather shaggy airedale, seen leaving No. 11 Downing street, who they think may be able to help with their inquiries."

Daily Express, Aug. 11th ,1970

"Whatever makes you think George minded missing his first match of the season to take us to see
The Tales of Beatrix Potter, Auntie?"

Sunday Express, Aug.15th, 1971

"I don't mind you entering, Agnes, but damn it - you might have told me you were eligible again."

Daily Express, Aug. 24th, 1971

"For gawd's sake don't tap on the counter to draw her attention - she'll have you strung up high as a kite before you can say pint of mild."

Sunday Express, Sep. 7th, 1971

"This suspicious note you saw dropped, Sir. After exhaustive investigations by MI5 and our forensic experts it turned out to be a fruit gum wrapper."

Sunday Express, Oct. 3rd, 1971

"Virginia Wade didn't kick up all that row when she lost, Henrietta."

Daily Express, Mar. 7th, 1972

"Well, back to the old ironing board."

Daily Express, Mar. 1st, 1972

"Unlike Wimbledon, there's nothing in the rules to say they _can't_ advertise in the Open."

Sunday Express, Jul. 9th, 1972

"If they do let wives in to stay, my case'll give the screws a headache - I'm in for bigamy."

Sunday Express, Aug. 6th, 1972

"Softening up His Lordship as his team was clobbered yesterday before we remind him Auntie Milly has arrived for the week."

Sunday Express, Aug. 13th, 1972

"Mine's doing his training at home to make sure he's fit enough to walk back to work tomorrow."

Sunday Express, Aug. 20th, 1972

"Tell Cassanova I'd like a word in the study about those letters of his."

Daily Express, Aug. 22nd, 1972

"Dinger, we learn from the grapevine that your Teddy Bear mascot contains four knuckle-dusters, two files and a hacksaw."

Daily Express, Aug. 29th, 1972

" I'll settle for a nice hot night club in exchange for training any time you like."

Sunday Express, Dec. 10th, 1972

"Tell your paper I deny any romance between me and Nurse Barker and there are no grounds for any rumours of a romance between us."

Sunday Express, Mar. 4th 1973

"Here comes the boy who cracked you with his umbrella."

Sunday Express, Mar. 18th, 1973

"Psst! If I informed you of the whereabouts of a £1 million IRA arms dump,
do you think we could let tour criminal charge of parking for ten minutes drop?"

Daily Express, Aug. 9th, 1973

"De-bagging the umpire after yesterday's decision didn't do you a lot of good."

"Wait till he takes his other sock off then we've got him."

Daily Express, Aug. 16th, 1973

"Hurt his toe kicking a policeman - what's the matter, my little angel' too hot?"

Daily Express, Aug. 28th, 1973

"Ladies! While I fully appreciate how grateful you are that your little ones have this week been returned to me . . ."

Daily Express, Sep. 4th, 1974

"There,s two of 'em who've had a decent harvest - my Building Society Manager and my Bank Manager."

Sunday Express, Sep. 16th, 1973

"He claims he's been wrongfully imprisoned as he was at least three feet away from Grandma's hat when the arrow penetrated."

Daily Express, Apr. 9th, 1974

"I'll bet if Sophia Loren wanted an X-ray of her gallstone there'd be a few blacklegs among you."

Daily Express, Aug. 1st, 1974

"Lady wants it in writing there are no bottom-spanking parties on board."

Sunday Express, Nov. 24th, 1974

"They all say the same - it's not so much they're fed up with the country,
they've had enough of Christmas holidays."

Sunday Express, Dec. 29th, 1974

"YOU DARE!"

Daily Express, Jan. 3rd, 1975

"Poor Algy, he was looking forward to going back to England with a Broken leg."

Daily Express, Jan. 16th 1975

"That was very public spirited of you to hop on the line and stop the Inter-City train for us.
Unfortunately we're just running into Ostend."

Daily Express, Mar. 7th, 1975

"You forget the golden rule of Father's Day - always let him win."

Sunday Express, Jun. 15th, 1975

"With the pound falling, milady, you can't go to Europe on holiday, so why not read about it?"

Daily Express, Jul. 4th, 1975

"Not that I'm suggesting anything, Vicar, but before you came by on the way to church there were five potatoes in this row, now there only be three."

Sunday Express, Jul. 20th, 1975

"Well, that seems a fairly painless way to get rid of 'em."

Daily Express, Sep. 16th, 1975

"Doctor doesn't consider you an emergency case.
Buying your boy a magic chemical set was a calculated risk."

Daily Express, Dec. 1st, 1975

"Cod fishing off the stern of an R.N. protection ship does nothing to relieve the tension between Iceland and the British Navy."

Daily Express, Dec. 9th, 1975

"You'll like our new secretary, sir, supplied under the new no-sex-discrimination Act."

Daily Express, Dec. 11th, 1975

"Just think Dad, if Graham Bell hadn't invented the Telephone a hundred years ago today
Auntie Bertha wouldn't be able to phone us to say they're all coming to tea this afternoon."

Sunday Express, Mar. 7th, 1976

"Mavis, that don't look like you're consoling one of 'em turned into a prince - that look exactly like consoling
Willie Boggis the cowman."

Daily Express, Apr. 13th, 1976

" I'd watch that 'Morning duckie' stuff, Hartley - it could get you a couple of chapters in her memoirs."

Daily Express, Jun. 15th, 1976

"Whoops! I thought he was going to topple over again."

Sunday Express, Jun. 20th, 1976

"You heard correctly, madam. I DID say I would rather fly to the States inside that whale, than in the same plane as you and your revolting children."

"Here comes our very own doyen of industry - graduated in the Christmas Play from a King of Orient to a Poor Shepherd in half a term."

Daily Express, Nov. 25th, 1976

"You go first and ask her if she wants any help with the housework - I tried it yesterday."

Daily Express, Dec. 2nd, 1976

"Your father has epitomised the entire collection in his usual sensitive, lucid way - 'Load of rubbish!'"

Sunday Express, Jan. 30th, 1977

"Don't build up too much hope, lads. He not only knows his rights on sex-discrimination laws, but my wife has the casting vote."

Daily Express, Jan. 11th, 1977

"Dammit, old boy - that isn't cricket!"

Daily Express, Jan. 18th, 1977

"If you really are going to put your head in the gas oven, darling, be a dear and do it before April 1st."

Daily Express, Mar. 16th, 1977

"I didn't say I hadn't got any confidence in any of 'em - my puppet said
he hadn't, got any confidence in any of 'em."

Daily Express, Mar. 21st, 1977

"Must hide those before she sees them or she'll put the bloody rent up."

Daily Express, Mar. 26th, 1977

"Four days' honeymoon in London Airport isn't a great start to a life of matrimonial bliss"

Daily Express, Apr. 11th, 1977

"Mind you, it involves studying hard for years under an employer before you publish a book on all the muck you have collected about him."

Daily Express, Apr. 22nd, 1977

"Now we come to the delicate exercise of choosing one of 'em to be hon. treasurer."

Daily Express, Apr. 25th, 1977

"We believe British industry should harness the enthusiasm, imagination and zest of youth."

Daily Express, Aug. 8th, 1977

"She saw them on TV chanting 'We want to work'."

Sunday Express, Aug. 28th, 1977

"I fell for that one - I let him have compassionate leave because his wife's going to have a baby.
Now he tells me he won't know if it's a boy or a girl till nine months' time."

Daily Express, Sep. 9th, 1977

"Not TOO dangerously, Boy."

"Grandma doesn't mind them naming churches and cathedrals after her,
but I don't think she'll go a lot on sex-mad giraffes."

Sunday Express, Oct. 22nd, 1977

"HRH is in one of his doom-watch moods this morning - hear that rude little word from below when you muffed that ?"

Sunday Express, Oct. 30th, 1977

Only the Giles' kids could get into such a jam...

"We had a nice quiet Christmas thanks to the firemen still being on strike."

Daily Express, Dec. 27th, 1977

"I *did* do everything I could to prevent you having an accident - I told you not to take the car."

Daily Express, Mar. 1st, 1978

"Lady says Boggis's Best Axle Oil always does her knee good and her mother's, and *her* mother's before her."

"I fear anything in my sermon will be beyond their understanding unless it refers to Red Rum."

Sunday Express, Apr. 2nd, 1978

"I doubt ye'll get cups of tea in the nick from the wee Argentinos if you go thumping the opponents after the match."

Sunday Express, May 21st, 1978

"She didn't go much on the merchandise, but I sold her all your £s for 90p."

Daily Express, Aug. 24th, 1978

"Ah! There you are Harold - the new Minister for Marriage has popped in to see us."

Daily Express, Feb. 1st, 1979

"We found it at the back of a car park. The man on TV showed us how to pick the lock."

Daily Express, Mar. 15th 1978

"So much for the 'Dress to thrill in Aristos slinky, body-hugging clothes' - Baked beans, egg 'n' chips three times."

"Football all day yesterday - non-stop cricket today - he'll tire himself out for his day of action on Wednesday."

Sunday Express, May 11th, 1980

" I've been in and out of here for 60-odd years and I'm hanged if I can remember the last time she told us her prices had gone down."

Daily Express, Jul. 12th. 1979

"Check watches, Miss Medler. I'm just off for a Rosie Lee."

"Look here, Edwards, we can't spend forty five minutes with each member of the public and then discover they're a 'don't know'."

Sunday Express, Apr. 8th, 1979

"He doesn't know I took a lovely picture of him with his Teddy Bear at Longleat."

Daily Express, May. 29th, 1979

"He's leaving home to live on the trains for a few days while they're still running."

NUR
Strike
OVER

ASLEF
Strike
starts
Saturday

Daily Express, Jul. 1st, 1982

"In view of the public's waning interest in boat races I asked cox how she felt about going topless"

Daily Express, Mar. 8th 1983

"Couldn't you just wear it down to the club to please them?"

Sunday Express, Jun. 21st, 1981

" I'm afraid that whale the gentleman's been giving the kiss-of-life to for
the last half hour happens to be one of these 'ere rubber ones."

Daily Express, Jul. 21st, 1981

"The race Rodney is describing is out of that window. There's a topless bathing pool outside the other."

Daily Express, Aug. 5th, 1980

"Remember the row he kicked up this morning about not going to miss his Test Match?"

"There'll be a wind of war right here if you don't get him out of Grandma's chair."

Sunday Express, Sep. 11th 1983

"If he sings We'll Meet Again once more, he'll be needing that flaming tin helmet!"

Daily Express, May 10th, 1985